THE NEST ON THE TWIG

THE TREE IN THE WOOD

Book 2

By the same editors

THE TREE IN THE WOOD
A Junior Anthology

THE NEST
ON THE TWIG

Poems chosen by
RAYMOND O'MALLEY
& DENYS THOMPSON

Decorations by Julia Ball

THE TREE IN THE WOOD: BOOK 2

FRANKLIN WATTS, INC.
575 Lexington Avenue
New York, N.Y. 10022

Copyright © Chatto and Windus Ltd 1966
Library of Congress Catalog Card Number: 68-19242

Published 1966 by
Chatto and Windus Ltd, London
First American Publication 1968
by Franklin Watts, Inc.
1 2 3 4

j 808.1
054ne

Printed in the U.S.A.

CONTENTS

§ 1

§ 2

§ 8

The egg was in the nest,
The nest was on the twig,
The twig was on the bough,
The bough was on the tree,
The tree was in the wood:
And the green grass grew all round,
around, around,
And the green grass grew all round.

The Cuckoo Comes

This is the day
When cuckoos sing,
And people say
Here comes Spring.
But wise birds stay
With guarding breasts
On Cuckoo-day
To save their nests.

ELEANOR FARJEON

I went to Noke

I went to Noke
But nobody spoke;
I went to Thame,
It was just the same;
Burford and Brill
Were silent and still,
But I went to Beckley
And they spoke directly.

Robin the Bobbin

Robin the Bobbin,
    the big-bellied Ben,
He ate more meat
    than fourscore men;
He ate a cow,
    he ate a calf,
He ate a butcher
    and a half,
He ate a church,
    he ate a steeple,
He ate a priest
    and all the people!
A cow and a calf,
An ox and a half,
A church and a steeple,
And all the good people,
And yet he complained
    that his stomach wasn't full.

The Nest

I watched a nest from day to day,
  A green nest full of pleasant shade,
  Wherein three speckled eggs were laid:
But when they should have hatched in May,
  The two old birds had grown afraid
Or tired, and flew away.

CHRISTINA ROSSETTI

My Mother Said

  My mother said
  I never should
Play with the gypsies in the wood.

  The wood was dark;
  The grass was green;
In came Sally with a tambourine.

  I went to the sea —
  no ship to get across;
I paid ten shillings for a blind white horse;

  I up on his back
  and was off in a crack,
Sally, tell my mother I shall never come back.

Tom, Tom, the Piper's Son

Tom, Tom, the piper's son,
He learned to play when he was young,
But all the tunes that he could play
Was, 'Over the hills and far away';
    Over the hills, and a great way off,
    And the wind will blow my top-knot off.

Now, Tom with his pipe made such a noise,
That he pleased both the girls and boys,
And they stopped to hear him play
'Over the hills and far away.'
    Over the hills, and a great way off,
    And the wind will blow my top-knot off.

Tom with his pipe did play with such skill,
That those who heard him could never keep still;
Whenever they heard they began for to dance—
Even pigs on their hind legs would after him prance.
    Over the hills, and a great way off,
    And the wind will blow my top-knot off.

Summer Evening

The sandy cat by the Farmer's chair
Mews at his knee for dainty fare;
Old Rover in his moss-greened house
Mumbles a bone, and barks at a mouse;
In the dewy fields the cattle lie
Chewing the cud 'neath a fading sky;
Dobbin at manger pulls his hay:
Gone is another summer's day.

WALTER DE LA MARE

No Answer

There was an Old Man who said, 'Well!
Will *nobody* answer this bell?
  I have pulled day and night,
  Till my hair has grown white,
But nobody answers this bell!'

EDWARD LEAR

The Farmyard

Up was I on my father's farm
  On a May day morning early,
Feeding of my father's sheep
  On a May day morning early.
With a baa baa here, and a baa baa there,
Here a baa, there a baa,
  Here a pretty baa!
Six pretty maids come again along with me
  To the merry green fields and the farmyard.

Up was I on my father's farm
  On a May day morning early,
Feeding of my father's cows
  On a May day morning early.
With a moo moo here, and a moo moo there,
Here a moo, there a moo,
  Here a pretty moo!
Six pretty maids come again along with me
To the merry green fields and the farmyard.

Up was I on my father's farm
  On a May day morning early,
Feeding of my father's hens
  On a May day morning early.
With a cluck cluck here, and a cluck cluck there,
Here a cluck, there a cluck,
  Here a pretty cluck!
Six pretty maids come again along with me
To the merry green fields and the farmyard

Up was I on my father's farm
  On a May day morning early,
Feeding of my father's ducks
  On a May day morning early.
With a quack quack here, and a quack quack there,
Here a quack, there a quack,
  Here a pretty quack!
Six pretty maids come again along with me
To the merry green fields and the farmyard.

*And so on, with goats (nan, nan), pigs (oik, oik),
geese (hiss, hiss), dogs (woof, woof), cats (miaow,
miaow) and whatever other creatures catch your fancy.*

What Folks are made of

What are little boys made of, made of?
  What are little boys made of?
Piggins and pails and little puppy tails,
  That's what little boys are made of.

What are little girls made of, made of?
  What are little girls made of?
Sugar and spice and all things nice
  And that's what little girls are made of.

What are young men made of, made of?
  What are young men made of?
Thorns and briars, they're all bad liars,
  And that's what young men are made of.

What are young women made of, made of?
  What are young women made of?
Rings and jings and all fine things,
  And that's what young women are made of.

What are old men made of, made of?
  What are old men made of?
Whisky and brandy and sugar and candy,
  And that's what old men are made of.

What are old women made of, made of?
  What are old women made of?
Moans and groans in their old aching bones,
  And that's what old women are made of.

What are little babies made of, made of?
  What are little babies made of?
Sugar and crumbs and all sweet things,
  And that's what little babies are made of.

The Little Mouse

The little mouse
Climbed the candlestick
To eat the tallow
Around the wick.

But when he got up,
He could not get down;
He called his grandmother,
But she was gone.

Then he turned himself
Into a ball,
His little sharp nose
And tail and all,

And rolled right down
Without any fuss,
And went some place else,
That little mouse!

PADRAIC COLUM

Think Again

'Who are you?'
Says One to Two;
Says Two to One 'I'm plenty;'
'Think again!'
Says little Ten,
And, 'Think again!' says Twenty.

W. B. RANDS

This is the Key

This is the key of the kingdom:
In that kingdom there is a city.
In that city there is a town.
In that town there is a street.
In that street there is a lane.
In that lane there is a yard.
In that yard there is a house.
In that house there is a room.
In that room there is a bed.
On that bed there is a basket.
In that basket there are some flowers.
Flowers in a basket.
Basket in the bed.
Bed in the room.
Room in the house.
House in the yard.
Yard in the lane.
Lane in the street.
Street in the town.
Town in the city.
City in the kingdom.
Of the kingdom this is the key.

The Snail

The horned snail so hates the drought
She quite seals up her shell,
But in the wet she crawls about,
As gardeners can tell.

She eats the juicy seedling shoots,
And cabbages and peas,
And then she hides besides the roots,
As close as she can squeeze.

For if a thrush comes hopping round
And spies her out, he'll beat her
With his hard bill upon the ground,
And having cracked, he'll eat her.

E. L. M. KING

The Snail

When bordering pinks and roses bloom,
And every garden breathes perfume;
When with huge figs the branches bend;
When clusters from the vine depend:
The snail looks round on flower and tree,
And cries, 'All these were made for me!'

JOHN GAY

The Silly

My daddy is dead, and I can't tell you how;
He left me six horses to follow the plough:
  With my *Whim, wham, waddle, oh!*
  Strim, stram, straddle, oh!
  Blowsey boys, bubble, oh,
  Over the brow!

I sold my six horses and bought me a cow;
To make me a fortune though I didn't know how:
  With my *Whim, wham* . . .

I sold my old cow and bought me a calf,
For I never made bargain but lost the best half:
  With my *Whim, wham* . . .

I bartered my calf and bought me a cat,
To sit at the fire and to warm her small back:
  With my *Whim, wham* . . .

I sold my small cat and bought me a mouse,
And with flame in his tail he burnt down my house:
  With my *Whim, wham, waddle, oh!*
  Strim, stram, straddle, oh!
  Blowsey boys, bubble, oh,
  Over the brow!

Miss T.

It's a very odd thing—
    As odd as can be—
That whatever Miss T. eats
    Turns into Miss T.;
Porridge and apples,
    Mince, muffins and mutton,
Jam, junket, jumbles—
    Not a rap, not a button
It matters; the moment
    They're out of her plate,
Though shared by Miss Butcher
    And sour Mr. Bate;
Tiny and cheerful,
    And neat as can be,
Whatever Miss T. eats
    Turns into Miss T.

WALTER DE LA MARE

God Bless This House

God bless this house from thatch to floor,
The twelve apostles guard the door.
Four angels to my bed;
Gabriel stands at the head,
John and Peter at my feet,
All to watch me while I sleep.

Green Broom

There was an old man and he lived in the West
And his trade was a-cutting of broom, green broom;
He had but one son, and his name it was John,
And he li-èd abed till 'twas noon, bright noon,
And he li-èd abed till 'twas noon.

The old man arose and unto his son goes,
And he swore he'd set fire to his room, his room,
If he would not rise and unbutton his eyes
And away to the woods for green broom, green broom,
And away to the woods for green broom.

Then Jack he did rise and did sharpen his knives
And he went to the woods cutting broom, green broom;
To market and fair, crying everywhere:
'Oh fair maids, do you want any broom, green broom?
O fair maids, do you want any broom?'

A lady sat up in her window so high
And she heard Johnny crying green broom, green broom;
She sent for her maid and unto her she said:
'Oh, go fetch me the lad that cries broom, green broom,
Oh, go fetch me the lad that cries broom.'

Then John he came back and upstairs he did go
And he entered that fair lady's room, her room.
'Dear Johnny,' said she, 'Oh can you fancy me,
Will you marry a lady in bloom, in bloom?
Will you marry a lady in bloom?'

Then John gave consent and unto the church went,
And he married the lady in bloom, in bloom.
Said she: 'I protest there is none in the West
Is so good as the lad who sells broom, green broom,
Is so good as the lad who sells broom.'

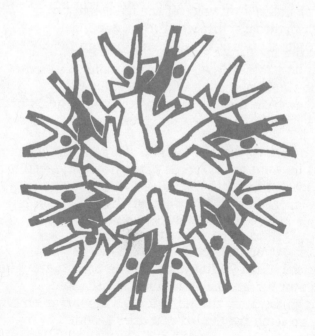

Ears Cocked

There's five of us in the family,
But only one who gobbles like mad
And grabs his coat at the sound of a train:
   That's Dad.

There's one who hears the smallest sneeze
And the other tell-tale sounds that come
From the cot upstairs or the pram outside:
   That's Mum.

A hoot, a whistle and a hoot again
To three of us mean nothing at all;
To two they mean, 'Hi, come and play':
   Me and Paul.

The cracked tin voice of the ice-cream van
On Saturdays, just when tea is done,
Brings the lot of us tumbling through the door—
   Bar one.

RAYMOND O'MALLEY

Oats and Beans and Barley Grow

Oats and beans and barley grow,
Oats and beans and barley grow.
Do you or I or anyone know
How oats and beans and barley grow?

A Bonnet Trimmed with Blue

I have a bonnet trimmed with blue.
Do you wear it? Yes I do!
I will wear it when I can
Over the sea to my young man.

My young man has gone to sea;
He'll come back and marry me.
Tip to the heel and tip to the toes:
That's the way the polka goes.

Horses

The horses of the sea
  Rear a foaming crest,
But the horses of the land
  Serve us the best.

The horses of the land
  Munch corn and clover,
While the foaming sea-horses
  Toss and turn over.

CHRISTINA ROSSETTI

London Bridge

London Bridge is broken down,
  Broken down, broken down,
London Bridge is broken down,
  My fair lady.

Build it up with wood and clay,
  Wood and clay, wood and clay,
Build it up with wood and clay,
  My fair lady.

Wood and clay will wash away,
  Wash away, wash away,
Wood and clay will wash away,
  My fair lady.

Build it up with bricks and mortar,
  Bricks and mortar, bricks and mortar,
Build it up with bricks and mortar,
  My fair lady.

Bricks and mortar will not stay,
  Will not stay, will not stay,
Bricks and mortar will not stay,
  My fair lady.

Build it up with iron and steel,
 Iron and steel, iron and steel,
Build it up with iron and steel,
 My fair lady.

Iron and steel will bend and bow,
 Bend and bow, bend and bow,
Iron and steel will bend and bow,
 My fair lady.

Build it up with silver and gold,
 Silver and gold, silver and gold,
Build it up with silver and gold,
 My fair lady.

Silver and gold will be stolen away,
 Stolen away, stolen away,
Silver and gold will be stolen away,
 My fair lady.

Build it up with stone so strong,
 Stone so strong, stone so strong,
Build it up with stone so strong,
 My fair lady.

The Moon

The moon has a face like the clock in the hall;
She shines on thieves on the garden wall,
On streets and fields and harbour quays,
And birds asleep in the forks of the trees.

The squalling cat and the squeaking mouse,
The howling dog by the door of the house,
The bat that lies in bed at noon,
All love to be out by the light of the moon.

But all of the things that belong to the day
Cuddle to sleep to be out of her way;
And flowers and children close their eyes
Till up in the morning the sun shall arise.

R. L. STEVENSON

The Chimney Sweeper

mother died I was very young,
ather sold me while yet my tongue
rcely cry ' 'weep! 'weep! 'weep! 'weep!'
chimneys I sweep, and in soot I sleep.

little Tom Dacre, who cried when his head,
rl'd like a lamb's back, was shaved: so I said
Tom! never mind it, for when your head's bare
ow that the soot cannot spoil your white hair.'

he was quiet, and that very night,
m was a-sleeping, he had such a sight!
thousands of sweepers, Dick, Joe, Ned, and Jack,
all of them locked up in coffins of black.

by came an Angel who had a bright key,
he opened the coffins and set them all free;
down a green plain leaping, laughing, they run,
wash in a river, and shine in the sun. . . .

WILLIAM BLAKE

Lost in a Shop

From the noisiest end of the crowded store—
Hear that! What a dismal wail!
A little lost girl, stood up on the counter,
As though she were there for sale!

An anxious shop-girl presses her hand;
Her tears fall thickly;
The anxious assistants stare all round . . .
Oh, come someone, and find her quickly!

JOHN WALSH

Picking Up Sticks

Last night the wind was up to tricks.
Let's to the wood to pick up sticks.

Last night the wind blew a chimney down.
There'll be scattered boughs in the beechwood brown.

Last night the wind broke a window-pane.
There'll be branches strewn on the heath again.

In town they are picking up tiles and bricks,
But *we*'ll to the wood to pick up sticks.

ELEANOR FARJEON

Fairy Song

You spotted snakes with double tongue,
   Thorny hedgehogs, be not seen;
Newts and blind-worms, do no wrong;
   Come not near our fairy queen.

     Philomel, with melody,
     Sing in our sweet lullaby;
  Lulla, lulla, lullaby; lulla, lulla, lullaby!
      Never harm,
      Nor spell nor charm,
    Come our lovely lady nigh.
    So, good night, with lullaby.

Weaving spiders, come not here;
   Hence, you long-legged spinners, hence!
Beetles black, approach not near;
   Worm nor snail, do no offence.

     Philomel, with melody,
     Sing in our sweet lullaby;
  Lulla, lulla, lullaby; lulla, lulla, lullaby!
      Never harm,
      Nor spell nor charm,
    Come our lovely lady nigh.
    So, good night, with lullaby.

WILLIAM SHAKESPEARE

Philomel, nightingale

32

Whip

Now Cape Clear it is
We'll be off Holyhead
And we'll shape our cou
Oh, Jenny, get your oat-

Now my boys, we're off
No more salt beef, no mor
One man in the chains for
Oh, Jenny, get your oat-cak

Now, my lads, we're round t
All hammocks lashed and all
We'll haul her into the Waterl
Oh, Jenny, get your oat-cake d

Now, my lads, we're all in dock,
We'll be off to Dan Lowrie's on
And now we'll have a good round
Oh, Jenny get your oat-cake done

When my
And my
Could sc
So your

There's
That cu
'Hush,
You kn

And so
As To
That
Were

And
And
The
And

33

Cattle in trucks

Poor cows, poor sheep,
I weep, I weep
To see you packed so tight;
While nought you know
Of where you go
By empty day and night.

Such noise, such heat,
Such weary feet,
No single thing you know.
No rest, no grass,
Only alas!
Your friends as scared as you.

I wish, I wish,
O how I wish,
That you could understand
That all is well;
You go to dwell
In some far pasture land.

E. L. M. KING

35

There Was a Naughty Boy

There was a naughty boy,
And a naughty boy was he,
He ran away to Scotland
The people for to see—
Then he found
That the ground
Was as hard,
That a yard
Was as long,
That a song
Was as merry,
That a cherry
Was as red,
That lead
Was as weighty,
That fourscore
Was eighty,
That a door
Was as wooden
As in England—
So he stood in his shoes
And he wondered,
He wondered,
He stood in his shoes
And he wondered.

JOHN KEATS

Snow

When winter winds blow
Hedges to and fro
And the flapping crow
Has gone to his home long ago,
Then I know
Snow
Will quietly fall, grow
Overnight higher than houses below,
Stop the stream in its flow,
And so
In a few hours, show
Itself man's ancient foe.
O
How slow
Is the silent gathering of snow.

LEONARD CLARK

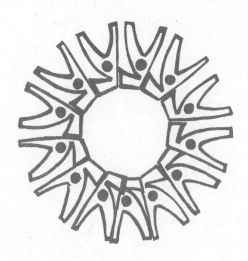

37

The Guinea-pig

There was a little guinea-pig,
Who, being little, was not big;
He always walked upon his feet,
And never fasted when he eat.

When from a place he ran away,
He never at that place did stay;
And while he ran, as I am told,
He ne'er stood still for young or old.

He often squeaked and sometimes vi'lent,
And when he squeaked he ne'er was silent;
Though ne'er instructed by a cat,
He knew a mouse was not a rat.

One day, as I am certified,
He took a whim and fairly died;
And as I'm told by men of sense,
He never has been living since.

certified, told

Nose, Nose

'Nose, nose, jolly red nose,
And who gave thee this jolly red nose?' —

'Nutmegs and ginger, cinnamon and cloves,
And they gave me this jolly red nose.'

BEAUMONT AND FLETCHER

Trotty Wagtail

Little trotty wagtail he went in the rain,
And tittering, tottering sideways he ne'er got straight again,
He stooped to get a worm, and looked up to get a fly,
And then he flew away ere his feathers they were dry.

Little trotty wagtail, he waddled in the mud,
And left his little footmarks, trample where he would;
He waddled in the water-pudge, and waggle went his tail,
And chirruped up his wings to dry upon the garden rail.

Little trotty wagtail, you nimble all about,
And in the dimpling water-pudge you waddle in and out;
Your home is nigh at hand, and in the warm pig-stye,
So little Master Wagtail, I'll bid you a goodbye.

JOHN CLARE

The Brook

I come from haunts of coot and hern,
   I make a sudden sally,
And sparkle out among the fern,
   To bicker down a valley. . . .

I chatter over stony ways,
   In little sharps and trebles,
I bubble into eddying bays,
   I babble on the pebbles. . . .

I slip, I slide, I gloom, I glance,
   Among my skimming swallows;
I make the netted sunbeams dance
   Against my sandy shallows.

I murmur under moon and stars
   In brambly wildernesses;
I linger by my shingly bars;
   I loiter round my cresses;

And out again I curve and flow
   To join the brimming river:
For men may come and men may go,
   But I go on for ever.

ALFRED TENNYSON

Kings

King Canute
  Sat down by the sea,
Up washed the tide
  And away went he.

Good King Alfred
  Cried, 'My sakes!
Not five winks,
  And look at those cakes!'

Lackland John
  Were a right royal Tartar
Till he made his mark
  Upon *Magna Carta*:

Ink, seal, table,
  On Runnymede green,
Anno Domini
  12—15.

WALTER DE LA MARE

The Owl and the Pussy-Cat

The Owl and the Pussy-Cat went to sea
   In a beautiful pea-green boat,
They took some honey, and plenty of money,
   Wrapped up in a five-pound note.
The Owl looked up to the stars above,
   And sang to a small guitar,
'O lovely Pussy! O Pussy, my love,
   What a beautiful Pussy you are,
     You are,
     You are!
   What a beautiful Pussy you are!'

Pussy said to the Owl, 'You elegant fowl!
   How charmingly sweet you sing!
O let us be married! too long we have tarried
   But what shall we do for a ring?'
They sailed away for a year and a day,
   To the land where the Bong-tree grows,
And there in a wood a Piggy-wig stood,
   With a ring at the end of his nose,
     His nose,
     His nose,
   With a ring at the end of his nose.

'Dear Pig, are you willing to sell for one shilling
  Your ring?' Said the Piggy, 'I will.'
So they took it away, and were married next day
  By the Turkey who lives on the hill.
They dined on mince, and slices of quince,
  Which they ate with a runcible spoon;
And hand in hand, on the edge of the sand,
  They danced by the light of the moon,
    The moon,
    The moon,
  They danced by the light of the moon.

EDWARD LEAR

Hurt No Living Thing

Hurt no living thing:
  Ladybird, nor butterfly,
Nor moth with dusty wing,
  Nor cricket chirping cheerily,
Nor grasshopper so light of leap,
  Nor dancing gnat, nor beetle fat,
Nor harmless worms that creep.

CHRISTINA ROSSETTI

Apple-Tree Rhyme

(To be sung in orchards, at the New Year)

Here stands a good apple tree;
Stand fast at root,
Bear well at top;
Every little twig
Bear an apple big;
Every little bough
Bear an apple now;
Hats full! caps full!
Three-score sacks full!
Hullo, boys! hullo!

Autumn Fires

In the other gardens
   And all up the vale,
From the autumn bonfires
   See the smoke trail!

Pleasant summer over
   And all the summer flowers,
The red fire blazes,
   The grey smoke towers.

Sing a song of seasons!
   Something bright in all!
Flowers in the summer,
   Fires in the fall!

R. L. STEVENSON

Blue Bell

I had a little dog and his name was Blue Bell,
I gave him some work, and he did it very well;
I sent him upstairs to pick up a pin,
He stepped in the coal-scuttle up to his chin;
I sent him to the garden to pick some sage,
He tumbled down and fell in a rage;
I sent him to the cellar to draw a pot of beer,
He came up again and said there was none there.

The Windmill

Behold! a giant am I!
  Aloft here in my tower,
  With my granite jaws I devour
The maize and the wheat and the rye,
  And grind them into flour.

I look down over the farms;
  In the fields of grain I see
  The harvest that is to be,
And I fling to the air my arms,
  For I know it is all for me.

I hear the sound of flails
  Far off, from the threshing-floors
  In barns, with their open doors,
And the wind, the wind in my sails,
  Louder and louder roars.

I stand here in my place,
    With my foot on the rock below,
    And whichever way it may blow
I meet it face to face,
    As a brave man meets his foe.

And while we wrestle and strive,
    My master, the miller, stands
    And feeds me with his hands;
For he knows who makes him thrive,
    Who makes him lord of lands.

On Sundays I take my rest;
    Church-going bells begin
    Their low, melodious din;
I cross my arms on my breast,
    And all is peace within.

HENRY WADSWORTH LONGFELLOW

What Can the Matter Be?

Oh, dear! what can the matter be?
Dear, dear! what can the matter be?
Oh, dear! what can the matter be?
Johnny's so long at the fair.

He promised to buy me a fairing should please me,
And then for a kiss, oh, he said he would tease me,
He promised to bring me a bunch of blue ribbons
To tie up my bonny brown hair.

And it's oh, dear! what can the matter be?
Dear, dear! what can the matter be?
Oh, dear! what can the matter be?
Johnny's so long at the fair.

He promised to bring me a basket of posies,
A garland of lilies, a garland of roses,
A little straw hat, to set off the blue ribbons
That tie up my bonny brown hair.

And it's oh, dear! what can the matter be?
Dear, dear! what can the matter be?
Oh, dear! what can the matter be?
Johnny's so long at the fair.

Sweet and Low

Sweet and low, sweet and low,
  Wind of the western sea,
Low, low, breathe and blow,
  Wind of the western sea!
Over the rolling waters go,
Come from the dying moon, and blow,
  Blow him again to me;
While my little one, while my pretty one, sleeps.

Sleep and rest, sleep and rest,
  Father will come to thee soon;
Rest, rest, on mother's breast,
  Father will come to thee soon;
Father will come to his babe in the nest,
Silver sails all out of the west
  Under the silvery moon;
Sleep, my little one, sleep, my pretty one, sleep.

ALFRED TENNYSON

There Was a Monkey

There was a monkey climbed up a tree,
When he fell down, then down fell he.

There was a crow sat on a stone,
When he was gone, then there was none.

There was an old wife did eat an apple,
When she'd eat two, she'd eat **a** couple.

There was a horse a-going to the mill,
When he went on, he stood not still.

There was a butcher cut his thumb,
When it did bleed, the blood did come.

There was a lackey ran a race,
When he ran fast, he ran apace.

There was a navy went into Spain,
When it returned, it came again.

Mick

Mick my mongrel-O
Lives in a bungalow,
Painted green with a round doorway.
  With an eye for cats
  And a nose for rats
He lies on his threshold half the day.
  He buries his bones
  By the rockery stones,
And never, oh never, forgets the place.
  Ragged and thin
  From his tail to his chin,
He looks at you with a sideways face.
  Dusty and brownish,
  Wicked and clownish,
He'll win no prize at the County Show.
  But throw him a stick,
  And up jumps Mick,
And right through the flower-beds see him go!

JAMES REEVES

The Ferryman

'Ferry me across the water,
  Do, boatman, do.'
'If you've a penny in your purse,
  I'll ferry you.'

'I have a penny in my purse,
  And my eyes are blue;
So ferry me across the water,
  Do, boatman, do.'

'Step into my ferry-boat,
  Be they black or blue,
And for the penny in your purse
  I'll ferry you.'

CHRISTINA ROSSETTI

If All the World Were Paper

If all the world were paper,
  And all the sea were ink,
If all the trees were bread and cheese,
  What should we have to drink?

If friars had no bald pates,
  Nor nuns had no dark cloisters,
If all the seas were beans and peas,
  What should we do for oysters?

Nurse's Song

When the voices of children are heard on the green,
  And laughing is heard on the hill,
My heart is at rest within my breast,
  And everything else is still.
'Then come home, my children, the sun is gone down,
  And the dews of night arise;
Come, come, leave off play, and let us away,
  Till the morning appears in the skies.'

'No, no, let us play, for it is yet day,
  And we cannot go to sleep;
Besides, in the sky the little birds fly,
  And the hills are all covered with sheep.'
'Well, well, go and play till the light fades away,
  And then go home to bed.'
The little ones leaped, and shouted, and laughed,
  And all the hills echoèd.

WILLIAM BLAKE

The Little Woman and the Pedlar

There was a little woman,
　As I have heard tell,
She went to market
　Her eggs for to sell;
She went to market
　All on a market day,
And she fell asleep
　On the king's highway.

There came by a pedlar,
　His name was Stout,
He cut her petticoats
　All round about;
He cut her petticoats
　Up to her knees;
Which made the little woman
　To shiver and sneeze.

When this little woman
　Began to awake,
She began to shiver,
　And she began to shake;
She began to shake,
　And she began to cry,
Lawk a mercy on me,
　This is none of I!

But if this be I,
   As I do hope it be,
I have a little dog at home
   And he knows me;
If it be I,
   He'll wag his little tail,
And if it be not I
   He'll loudly bark and wail!

Home went the little woman
   All in the dark,
Up starts the little dog,
   And he began to bark;
He began to bark,
   And she began to cry,
Lawk a mercy on me,
   This is none of I!

I is for Idle in Yorkshire

In Idle
In Yorks
Nobody
Works,
The Cook drops
The ladle,
The Gardener
The hoe,
The Nurse
Leaves the cradle,
Dog Toby
His show,
The Smith drops his hammer,
The Schoolboy his grammar,
The Groom drops his bridle,
The Maid
Knives and forks—
Nobody works,
Boys saunter,
Girls sidle,
Everyone's idle,
In Idle,
In Yorks.

ELEANOR FARJEON

Three Pigs

There was an old sow, she lived in a sty,
  And three little piggies had she.
She waddled around saying 'Onk, onk, onk,'
  While the little ones said, 'Wee wee!'

'My dear little brothers,' said one of the brats,
  'My dear little piggies,' said he,
'Let us all in the future say, "Onk, onk, onk,"
  It's so childish to say, "Wee wee!"'

Now these little piggies grew skinny and lean;
  And lean they might very well be,
For somehow they couldn't say, 'Onk, onk, onk,'
  And they wouldn't say, 'Wee, wee, wee!'

Now these little piggies they up and died,
  They died of the Fee-lo-dee-zee
From trying too hard to say, 'Onk, onk, onk!'
  When they only should say, 'Wee, wee!'

Beardful

There was an Old Man with a beard,
Who said, 'It is just as I feared!
  Two Owls and a Hen,
  Four Larks and a Wren,
Have all built their nests in my beard!'

EDWARD LEAR

57

Mouse

Mouse, mouse who lives in our house,
Scurrying by on your velvety feet,
Silently scuttling from dresser to table,
What have you found to eat?

    'Cake crumbs and butter,
    Biscuits and batter,
    Apples and oranges,
    Pears and potatoes,
    Cheese ripe and mellow,
    Pineapples yellow,
    Platter on platter
    Of juicy tomatoes.'

Mouse, mouse who lives in our house
In the hole in the wainscot under the sink,
When you've eaten your fill of golden potatoes
What do you find to drink?

    'Clear, sparkling water
    From the tap in the kitchen,
    Cool, sweetened tea
    As brown as stones,
    Bottles of pop
    That fizz without stop,
    Soup that is rich in
    The savour of bones.'

Mouse, mouse who lives in our house,
With an eye and a nose for the food in our larder,
Now that we know what you dine on and wine on,
You'll find that evading our pussy's much harder.

DAVID SHAVREEN

Hark! hark! the lark

Hark! hark! the lark at heaven's gate sings,
   And Phoebus 'gins arise,
His steeds to water at those springs
   On chaliced flowers that lies;
And winking Mary-buds begin
   To ope their golden eyes;
With every thing that pretty is,
   My lady sweet, arise!
     Arise, arise!

WILLIAM SHAKESPEARE

The Intruder

Two-boots in the forest walks,
Pushing through the bracken stalks.

Vanishing like a puff of smoke,
Nimbletail flies up the oak.

Longears helter-skelter shoots
Into his house among the roots.

At work upon the highest bark,
Tapperbill knocks off to hark.

Painted-wings through sun and shade
Flounces off along the glade.

Not a creature lingers by,
When clumping Two-boots comes to pry.

JAMES REEVES

School's Out

Girls scream,
   Boys shout;
Dogs bark,
   School's out.

Cats run,
   Horses shy;
Into trees
   Birds fly.

Babes wake
   Open-eyed;
If they can,
   Tramps hide.

Old man,
   Hobble home;
Merry mites,
   Welcome.

W. H. DAVIES

A Day in the Country

Minnie and Mattie
   And fat little May,
Out in the country,
   Spending a day.

Such a bright day,
   With the sun glowing,
And the trees half in leaf,
   And the grass growing.

Pinky white pigling
   Squeals through his snout,
Woolly white lambkin
   Frisks all about.

Cluck! Cluck! the nursing hen
   Summons her folk,—
Ducklings all downy soft,
   Yellow as yolk.

Cluck! cluck! the mother hen
   Summons her chickens
To peck the dainty bits
   Found in her pickings.

Minnie and Mattie
   And May carry posies,
Half of sweet violets,
   Half of primroses.

Give the sun time enough,
  Glowing and glowing,
He'll rouse the roses
  And bring them blowing.

Don't wait for roses
  Losing today,
O Minnie, Mattie,
  And wise little May.

Violets and primroses
  Blossom today,
For Minnie and Mattie
  And fat little May.

CHRISTINA ROSSETTI

Some One

Some one came knocking
  At my wee, small door;
Some one came knocking,
  I'm sure—sure—sure;
I listened, I opened,
  I looked to left and right,
But nought there was a-stirring
  In the still dark night;
Only the busy beetle
  Tap-tapping in the wall,
Only from the forest
  The screech-owl's call,
Only the cricket whistling
  While the dewdrops fall,
So I know not who came knocking,
  At all, at all, at all.

WALTER DE LA MARE

A Dream Dreamed at Sevenoaks

Seven sweet singing birds up in a tree;
Seven swift sailing-ships white upon the sea;
Seven bright weathercocks shining in the sun;
Seven slim race-horses ready for a run;
Seven gold butterflies, flitting overhead;
Seven red roses blowing in a garden bed;
Seven white lilies, with honey bees inside them;
Seven round rainbows with clouds to divide them;
Seven nights running I dreamed it all plain;
With bread and jam for supper I could dream it all again!

W. B. RANDS

A Dream Dreamed at Nine-Elms

Nine clever conjurors eating hot coals;
Nine sturdy mountaineers leaping on their poles;
Nine little drummer-boys beating on their drums;
Nine fat aldermen sitting on their thumbs;
Nine new knockers to our front door;
Nine new neighbours that I never saw before;
Nine times running I dreamed it all plain;
With bread and cheese for supper I could dream it all again!

W. B. RANDS

Death of the Cat

Alas! Mowler, the children's pride,
has slipped on a water-butt, tumbled inside
and died.

The seamstress on her sewing machine
stitched a shroud of satin sheen.

The carpenter hammered and planed a coffin
of seasoned oak without a knot in.

The sexton—he loved dear Mowler well—
mournfully, mournfully tolled the bell.

Few were the prayers the parson spoke.
All he could do, poor fellow, was choke.

But saddest of all in the funeral train
were the children. Deep were their sorrow and pain,

for they knew, as they followed the churchyard through,
they'd never set eyes on Mowler again.

In silence behind the coffin they stepped,
solemnly, slowly. Everyone wept

except
the little mice hid in the hedge—not they!
'Twas not their hearts that bled.
'Let's out and play,'
they cried. 'Oh, spread
the butter thick on the bread!
Dance in cream cheese right up to our knees,
for the cat is dead!
Hooray!
The cat
　　　　is
　　　　　　dead!'

IAN SERRAILLIER

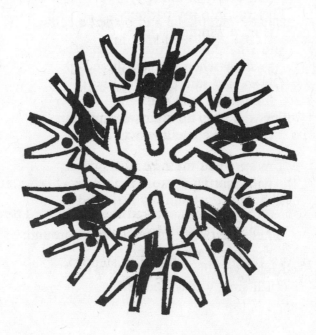

The Spider and the Fly

'Will you walk into my parlour?'
  said the Spider to the Fly;
' 'Tis the prettiest little parlour
  that ever you did spy;
The way into my parlour
  is up a winding stair
And I have many curious things
  to show when you are there.'
'Oh *no, no,*' said the little Fly;
  'to ask me is in vain;
For who goes up your winding stair
  can ne'er come down again.'

'I'm sure you must be weary, dear,
  with soaring up so high;
Will you rest upon my little bed?'
  said the Spider to the Fly.
'There are pretty curtains drawn around;
  the sheets are fine and thin;
And if you like to rest awhile
  I'll snugly tuck you in!'

'Oh, *no, no,*' said the little Fly;
  'for I've often heard it said,
They never, never wake again
  who sleep upon your bed!'

'Sweet creature!' said the Spider,
  'you are witty and you're wise;
How handsome are your gauzy wings,
  how brilliant are your eyes!
I have a little looking-glass
  upon my parlour shelf,
If you'll step in one moment, dear,
  you shall behold yourself.'
'I thank you, gentle sir,' she said,
  'for what you're pleased to say,
And bidding you good morning now,
  I'll call another day. . . .'

MARY HOWITT

Spring

Sound the Flute!
Now it's mute.
Birds delight
Day and Night;
Nightingale
In the dale,
Lark in Sky,
Merrily,
Merrily, Merrily, to welcome in the Year.

Little Lamb,
Here I am;
Come and lick
My white neck;
Let me pull
Your soft Wool;
Let me kiss
Your soft face:
Merrily, Merrily, we welcome in the Year.

WILLIAM BLAKE

Queen Mab's Waggon

She comes
In shape no bigger than an agate-stone
On the forefinger of an alderman,
Drawn with a team of little atomies
Athwart men's noses as they lie asleep:
Her waggon-spokes made of long spinners' legs;
The cover, of the wings of grasshoppers;
The traces, of the smallest spider's web;
The collars, of the moonshine's watery beams;
Her whip, of cricket's bone; the lash, of film;
Her waggoner, a small grey-coated gnat . . .
Her chariot is an empty hazel-nut,
Made by the joiner squirrel or old grub,
Time out o' mind the fairies' coach-makers.
And in this state she gallops night by night . . .

WILLIAM SHAKESPEARE

The Duck

If I were in a fairy tale,
And it were my good luck
To have a wish, I'd choose to be
A lovely snow-white duck.

When she puts off into the pond
And leaves me on the brink,
She wags her stumpy tail at me,
And gives a saucy wink,

Which says as plain as words could say
I'm safe as safe can be,
Stay there, or you will drown yourself,
The pond was made for me.

She goes a-sailing to and fro,
Just like a fishing-boat,
And steers and paddles all herself,
And never wets her coat.

Then in the water, upside down,
I've often seen her stand,
More neatly than the little boys
Who do it on the land.

And, best of all, her children are
The ducklings, bright as gold,
Who swim about the pond with her
And do as they are told.

E. L. M. KING

The Little Boat

'Twas such a little, little boat
That toddled down the bay!
'Twas such a gallant, gallant sea
That beckoned it away!

'Twas such a greedy, greedy wave
That licked it from the coast:
Nor ever guessed the stately sails
My little craft was lost!

EMILY DICKINSON

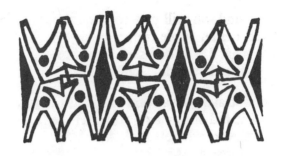

The Poor Couple

There was an old couple and they were poor;
They lived in a cottage that had but one door.
Oh, what a poor couple were they, were they,
Oh, what a poor couple were they!

This little old man went away from home
A-leaving his little old woman alone.
Oh, what a good man was he, was he,
Oh, what a good man was he!

This little old man he came home at last
And found that the door and the windows were fast.
'Oh, what is the matter?' said he, said he,
'Oh, what is the matter?' said he.

'Oh, I have been sick since you have been gone;
Had you been in the garden you'd hear me groan.'
'I'm sorry for that,' said he, said he,
'I'm sorry for that,' said he.

'Oh husband, oh will you do one thing for me?
Go fetch me an apple from yonder tree.'
'That's what I will do,' said he, said he,
'That's what I will do,' said he.

He went straight away and he clumb up the tree
His foot it did slippy and down fell he!
'That's cleverly done!' said she, said she,
'That's cleverly done!' said she.

This poor little man was a-carried to bed,
And with a blue ribbon they tied up his head.
'Oh, now I shall die,' he said, he said,
'Oh, now I shall die,' he said.

This poor little man, he sighed, he sighed,
And presently after he died, he died.
'I'm sorry for that!' she cried, she cried,
'I'm sorry for that!' she cried.

The Quartermaster's Stores

There's eggs, eggs,
That walk about on legs
    In the Quartermaster's stores.

There's steak, steak,
To keep us all awake
    In the Quartermaster's stores.

There's kippers, kippers,
That walk about in slippers
    In the Quartermaster's stores.

There's cake, cake,
To give us stomach ache
    In the Quartermaster's stores.

(And so on, to please yourself)

What's In There?

What's in there?
Gold and money.
Where's my share o't?
The mousie ran away wi't.
Where's the mousie?
In her housie.
Where's her housie?
In the wood.
Where's the wood?
The fire burnt it.
Where's the fire?
The water quenched it.
Where's the water?
The brown bull drank it.
Where's the brown bull?
Back o' Burnie's hill.
Where's Burnie's hill?
All clad with snow.
Where's the snow?
The sun melted it.
Where's the sun?
High, high up in the air!

The Ceremonial Band

The old King of Dorchester,
He had a little orchestra,
And never did you hear such a ceremonial band.
'Tootle-too,' said the flute,
'Deed-a-reedle,' said the fiddle,
For the fiddles and the flutes were the finest in the land.

The old King of Dorchester,
He had a little orchestra,
And never did you hear such a ceremonial band.
'Pump-a-rum,' said the drum,
'Tootle-too,' said the flute,
'Deed-a-reedle,' said the fiddle,
For the fiddles and the flutes were the finest in the land.

The old King of Dorchester,
He had a little orchestra,
And never did you hear such a ceremonial band.
'Pickle-pee,' said the fife,
'Pump-a-rum,' said the drum,
'Tootle-too,' said the flute,
'Deed-a-reedle,' said the fiddle,
For the fiddles and the flutes were the finest in the land.

The old King of Dorchester,
 He had a little orchestra,
And never did you hear such a ceremonial band.
 'Zoomba-zoom,' said the bass,
 'Pickle-pee,' said the fife,
 'Pump-a-rum,' said the drum,
 'Tootle-too,' said the flute,
 'Deed-a-reedle,' said the fiddle,
For the fiddles and the flutes were the finest in the land.

The old King of Dorchester,
 He had a little orchestra,
And never did you hear such a ceremonial band.
 'Pah-pa-rah,' said the trumpet,
 'Zoomba-zoom,' said the bass,
 'Pickle-pee,' said the fife,
 'Pump-a-rum,' said the drum,
 'Tootle-too,' said the flute,
 'Deed-a-reedle,' said the fiddle,
For the fiddles and the flutes were the finest in the land.
Oh! the fiddles and the flutes were the finest in the land.

JAMES REEVES

When I was a Lad

When I was a lad and so was my dad
I came out of a bean swad;
The bean swad it was too full
And I jumped into a roaring bull;
The roaring bull it was too fat
And I jumped into a gentleman's hat;
The gentleman's hat it was too fine
So I jumped into a bottle of wine;
The bottle of wine it was too clear
So I jumped into a barrel of beer;
The barrel of beer it was too thick
So I jumped out on an oak stick;
The oak stick began to crack
And I jumped onto a horse's back;
The horse's back began to bend
So I jumped down by a turkey hen;
The turkey hen began to lay
And I got an egg that day for my tay.

Colours

What is pink? a rose is pink
By the fountain's brink.
What is red? a poppy's red
In its barley bed.
What is blue? the sky is blue
Where the clouds float through.
What is white? a swan is white
Sailing in the light.
What is yellow? pears are yellow,
Rich and ripe and mellow.
What is green? the grass is green,
With small flowers between.
What is violet? clouds are violet
In the summer twilight.
What is orange? why, an orange,
Just an orange!

CHRISTINA ROSSETTI

The Old Woman and Her Pig

An old woman was coming home from market with a pig. The piggy would not go over a stile. She went a little farther, and she met a dog. So she said to the dog:

> 'Dog, dog, bite pig;
> Piggy won't get over the stile,
> And I shan't get home to-night!'

But the dog would not.

On she went a little farther, and she met a stick. So she said:

> 'Stick, stick, beat dog;
> Dog won't bite pig;
> Piggy won't get over the stile,
> And I shan't get home to-night!'

But the stick would not.

On she went a little farther, and she met a fire. So she said:

> 'Fire, fire, burn stick;
> Stick won't beat dog;
> Dog won't bite pig;
> Piggy won't get over the stile,
> And I shan't get home to-night!'

But the fire would not.

On she went a little farther, and she met some water. So she said:

> 'Water, water, quench fire;
> Fire won't burn stick;
> Stick won't beat dog;
> Dog won't bite pig;
> Piggy won't get over the stile,
> And I shan't get home to-night!'

But the water would not.

On she went a little farther, and she met an ox. So she said:

> 'Ox, ox, drink water;
> Water won't quench fire;
> Fire won't burn stick;
> Stick won't beat dog;
> Dog won't bite pig;
> Piggy won't get over the stile,
> And I shan't get home to-night!'

But the ox would not.

On she went a little farther, and she met a butcher. So she said:

> 'Butcher, butcher, kill ox;
> Ox won't drink water;
> Water won't quench fire;
> Fire won't burn stick;
> Stick won't beat dog;
> Dog won't bite pig;
> Piggy won't get over the stile,
> And I shan't get home to-night!'

But the butcher would not.

On she went a little farther, and she met a rope. So she said:

> 'Rope, rope, hang butcher;
> Butcher won't kill ox;
> Ox won't drink water;
> Water won't quench fire:
> Fire won't burn stick;
> Stick won't beat dog;
> Dog won't bite pig;
> Piggy won't get over the stile,
> And I shan't get home to-night!'

But the rope would not.

Then she went a little farther, and she met a rat. So she said:

> 'Rat, rat, gnaw rope;
> Rope won't hang butcher;
> Butcher won't kill ox;
> Ox won't drink water;
> Water won't quench fire;
> Fire won't burn stick;
> Stick won't beat dog;
> Dog won't bite pig;
> Piggy won't get over the stile,
> And I shan't get home to-night!'

But the rat would not.

On she went a little farther, and she met a cat. So she said:

> 'Cat, cat, kill rat;
> Rat won't gnaw rope;
> Rope won't hang butcher;
> Butcher won't kill ox;
> Ox won't drink water;

Water won't quench fire;
Fire won't burn stick;
Stick won't beat dog;
Dog won't bite pig;
Piggy won't get over the stile,
And I shan't get home to-night!'

The cat asked for a saucer of milk. When this at last was obtained:

The cat began to kill the rat;
The rat began to gnaw the rope;
The rope began to hang the butcher;
The butcher began to kill the ox;
The ox began to drink the water;
The water began to quench the fire;
The fire began to burn the stick;
The stick began to beat the dog;
The dog began to bite the pig;
The little pig in a fright jumped over the stile;
And the old woman got home that night!

Pleasures for John Keats

Two or three posies
  With two or three simples —
Two or three noses
  With two or three pimples —
Two or three wise men
  And two or three ninnies —
Two or three purses
  And two or three guineas —
Two or three cats
  And two or three mice —
Two or three sprats
  At a very great price —

Two or three smiles
  And two or three frowns —
Two or three miles
  To two or three towns —
Two or three pegs
  For two or three bonnets —
Two or three dove eggs
  To hatch into sonnets.

JOHN KEATS

Jack Jingle

Jack Jingle went 'prentice
    To make a horseshoe,
He washed the iron
    Till it would not do.
His master came in,
    And began for to rail;
Says Jack, 'The shoe's spoiled,
    But 'twill still make a nail.'

He tried at the nail,
    But, chancing to miss,
Says, 'If it won't make a nail,
    It shall yet make a hiss.'
Then into the water
    Threw the hot iron, smack.
'Hiss!' quoth the iron;
    'I thought so,' says Jack.

Bingo

There was an old dog and he lived at the mill,
　And Bingo was his name, sir.
　　B—I—N—G—O,
And Bingo was his name, sir.

　　Bang her and bop her, and kick her and kop her,
　　　For Bingo was his name, sir.
　　You sing, *bang her*, and I'll sing, *bop her*,
　　　And you sing, *kick her*, and I'll sing, *kop her*,
　　And bang her and bop her, and kick her and kop her,
　　　And Bingo was his name, sir.

The miller he bought him a barrel of ale,
　And called it right good Stingo.
　　S—T—I—N—G—O,
And called it right good Stingo.

　　Bang her and bop her, and kick her and kop her,
　　　He called it right good Stingo.
　　You sing, *bang her*, and I'll sing, *bop her*,
　　　And you sing, *kick her*, and I'll sing, *kop her*,
　　And bang her and bop her, and kick her and kop her,
　　　He called it right good Stingo.

The miller he went to town one day
And bought a wedding-ring O.
R—I—N—G—O,
And bought a wedding-ring O.

Bang her and bop her, and kick her and kop her,
He bought a wedding-ring O.
You sing, *bang her*, and I'll sing, *bop her*,
And you sing, *kick her*, and I'll sing, *kop her*,
And bang her and bop her, and kick her and kop her,
He bought a wedding-ring O.

Now is not this a pretty tale?
I swear it is by Jingo.
J—I—N—G—O,
I swear it is by Jingo.

Bang her and bop her, and kick her and kop her,
I swear it is by Jingo.
You sing, *bang her*, and I'll sing, *bop her*,
And you sing, *kick her*, and I'll sing, *kop her*,
And bang her and bop her, and kick her and kop her,
I swear it is, by Jingo.

Clean Clara

Clean Clara scrubs and sings.
She cleaned a hundred thousand things.

She cleaned the works of the eight-day clock,
She cleaned the spring of a secret lock;

She cleaned the mirror, she cleaned the cupboard;
All the books she India-rubbered!

She cleaned the keys of the harpsichord,
She cleaned my lady, she cleaned my lord.

She cleaned the cage of the cockatoo,
The oldest bird that ever grew.

She cleaned the china, she cleaned the delf;
She cleaned the baby, she cleaned herself!

Tomorrow morning she means to try
To clean the cobwebs from the sky;

Some people say the girl will rue it,
But my belief is she will do it.

W. B. RANDS

Index of First Lines

ACKNOWLEDGEMENTS

The editors make grateful acknowledgment to the following for permission to reprint copyright material:

Rupert Hart-Davis Limited for 'Snow' from Leonard Clark's *Daybreak*; Padraic Colum for 'The Little Mouse'; Mrs H. M. Davies and Jonathan Cape Ltd for 'School's Out' from the *Collected Poems* of W. H. Davies; The Literary Trustees of Walter de la Mare and the Society of Authors as their representative for 'Summer Evening', 'Miss T.', 'Kings' and 'Someone'; Harvard University Press for a poem from *The Poems of Emily Dickinson*; David Higham Associates Ltd for 'I is for Idle' from *Perkin the Pedlar*, 'The Cuckoo Comes' from *The Children's Bells* and 'Picking up Sticks' from *Country Child's Alphabet* by Eleanor Farjeon; Basil Blackwell for 'The Snail', 'Cattle in Trucks' and 'The Duck' by Mrs E. L. M. King; The Clarendon Press for 'The Guinea Pig' from *Lore and Language of Schoolchildren* by Iona and Peter Opie; James Reeves and Oxford University Press for 'The Intruder', 'Mick' and 'The Ceremonial Band' from *The Blackbird in the Lilac*; Ian Serraillier and Oxford University Press for 'Death of the Cat' from *The Tale of the Monster Horse*; David Shavreen for 'Mouse'; John Walsh and William Heinemann Ltd for 'Lost in a Shop' from *The Truants*; Novello & Co Ltd for 'The Poor Couple' which was collected by Cecil Sharp.

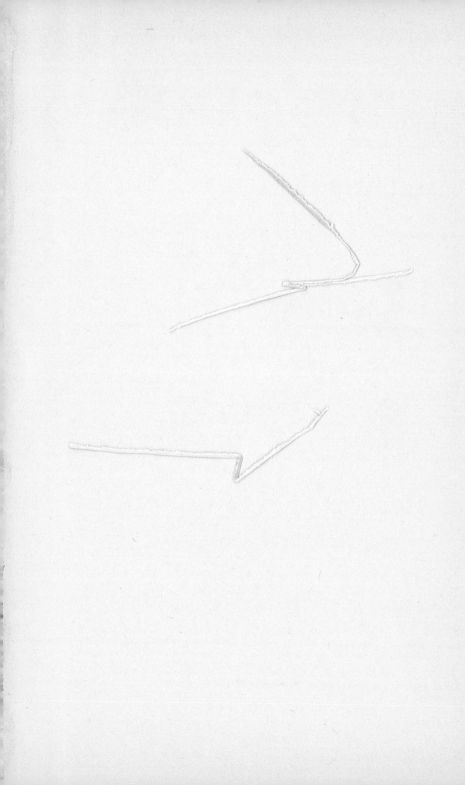